Military Vehicles

fotofax

SOVIET MECHANIZED FIREPOWER 1941–1945

Steven J. Zaloga and J. Magnuski

Front cover illustration: An ISU-122 heavy assault gun currently preserved in Poznan, Poland.

Back cover illustrations:
Top: An SU-76M light assault gun currently preserved at the Polish Army Museum in Warsaw.
Below: An ISU-152 currently preserved at the Red Army Museum in Leningrad. (Esa Muikku)

1. The YaG-10 heavy lorry was modified in the late 1930s to mount a 76.2mm Model 1931 anti-aircraft gun. During the fighting in 1941, it was used as often in the improvised anti-tank role as for air defence.

▼ 1

SOVIET
MECHANIZED
FIREPOWER
1941–1945

Steven J. Zaloga and J. Magnuski

ARMS AND
ARMOUR

▲ 2

2. The Russians developed assault guns in the pre-war years, like this AT-1 mounting a 76.2mm regimental gun, but they were not favoured by the artillery branch. The AT-1 programme was examined in 1938 with a view to giving the T-26 tank chassis more firepower, but no production ensued.

3. The only assault guns adopted by the Red Army before the Second World War were the so-called artillery tanks. These consisted of a turret derived from the T-28 medium tank, fitted to light tank hulls such as the T-26 or BT-7 fast tank. They were intended to supplement the small 45mm anti-tank gun of the light tanks. These artillery tanks were extremely rare, and this photograph is all the more curious as it shows a BT-7A artillery tank in Budapest in 1942 following its capture by Hungarian troops in the first year of the war. (Ivan Bajtos)

▼ 3

INTRODUCTION

First published in Great Britain in 1989 by Arms and Armour Press, Artillery House, Artillery Row, London SW1P 1RT.

Distributed in the USA by Sterling Publishing Co. Inc., 387 Park Avenue South, New York, NY 10016-8810.

Distributed in Australia by Capricorn Link (Australia) Pty. Ltd., P.O. Box 665, Lane Cove, New South Wales 2066, Australia.

British Library Cataloguing in Publication Data:
Zaloga, Steven J.
Soviet mechanized firepower 1941–1945.
1. Soviet Union. Military equipment
I. Title II. Magnuski, Janusz
III. Series
623'.0947
ISBN 1-85409-016-X

Designed and edited by DAG Publications Ltd. Designed by David Gibbons; edited by Michael Boxall; layout by Cilla Eurich; typeset by Ronset Typesetters Ltd, Darwen, Lancashire, and by Typesetters (Birmingham) Limited, Warley, West Midlands; camerawork by M&E Reproductions, North Fambridge, Essex; printed and bound in Great Britain by The Alden Press Limited, Oxford.
Line illustrations by Janusz Magnuski.

During the Second World War the Red Army was slow to adopt self-propelled artillery. Although small numbers of artillery support vehicles were in service in 1941, these were mainly assault tanks, not true mechanized artillery. The Russians noted the extensive German use of assault guns, like the ubiquitous StuG.III, and began to follow suit in 1942. Soviet wartime assault gun development is frequently misunderstood, often being labelled self-propelled artillery. Although the weapons on the vehicle may very well have been derived from artillery weapons, the resulting vehicles were not used by artillery troops. Assault guns were manned by troops trained by the Red Army's tank force, not artillery force, and used modified tank tactics. They were primarily used for direct fire, and many of the vehicles had no provision for the more traditional artillery indirect fire role. Soviet assault guns were used to supplement tanks, not towed artillery.

The light SU-76 assault gun was adopted as an infantry support vehicle, replacing the pre-war T-26 tank. It served either in the tank-destroyer role, or for direct gunfire support. It was far from adequate in the tank-destroyer role during the later years of the war, but the automotive factories which produced it were not capable of building heavier tracked vehicles. Its lack of overhead protection and thin armour were not popular, but it was better than nothing! This highlights the main attraction of assault guns. They were capable of carrying a larger weapon than the turreted tank from which they were derived. The T-70 had a 45mm gun, while its assault gun derivative, the SU-76, had a 76mm gun.

The medium assault guns, like the SU-85 and SU-100, were conceived purely as tank-destroyers. They were armed with larger guns than the medium tanks they were derived from, and so restored a measure of balance in the fighting against the thickly armoured German tanks of 1944–5. The heavy assault guns such as the SU-152, ISU-122 and ISU-152 were intended for both tank hunting and direct fire support. Soviet assault guns amounted to about 20 per cent of total wartime armoured vehicle production. They did not see extensive service until the winter of 1942–3 when the first experimental units were deployed on the Leningrad Front. At first, these were mixed SU-76 and SU-122 units. The mixture proved unsuccessful, leading to the formation of units with only a single type of assault gun. This set the pattern for later assault gun formations. Although called regiments, the assault gun units were quite small, with only 12–16 vehicles during the period 1943–4. These formations were usually under army control (equivalent of US or British corps), and were doled out to support rifle or tank divisions as circumstances demanded. In 1944, the first tank-destroyer battalions were formed, usually with 21 SU-85 or SU-100. The largest assault gun formations were the special Guards Brigades, frequently called breakthrough brigades. These were equipped with the heavy ISU-122 or ISU-152 and saw considerable combat in 1945 during the final months of the war.

Some of the wartime assault guns such as the SU-100 and ISU-152 remained in service with the Soviet Army or Warsaw Pact armies well into the 1960s. The Soviet Army largely dropped the assault gun concept by this time. In their place came a new generation of true artillery vehicles, such as the 2S1 and 2S3 in the early 1970s. These are covered in a companion volume in this series entitled *Soviet Mechanized Firepower Today*.

▲ 4

▲ 5 ▼ 6

4. The T-26A artillery tank was an infantry counterpart to the cavalry's BT-7A artillery tank. It was built in very small numbers, and saw limited fighting in 1941.

5. Due to the shortage of tanks in some areas in 1941, local factories began to make improvised armoured vehicles using agricultural tractors as the basis. This particular vehicle consisted of a KhTZ-5 tractor with a 45mm anti-tank gun added. Some T-20 Komsomolets armoured tractors had ZiS-29 57mm anti-tank guns attached to form the improvised ZiS-30 tank-destroyer.

6. The SU-14-2 assault gun was a pre-war project to adapt the B-10 152mm naval gun to an armoured chassis. Although it did not enter series production, the prototype was used in the defence of Moscow in 1941. (George Balin)

7. The KV-2 was a direct equivalent of the earlier T-26A and BT-7A artillery tanks. It mounted a 152mm howitzer in place of the 76mm gun carried on the normal 76mm KV-1 tank version. This is a KV-2 Model 1939 of the early production type which used a different turret configuration from the more common KV-2 Model 1940. It is most easily distinguished by the ribbed mantlet cover seen here. The KV-2 was very heavily armoured and gave the Germans a great deal of trouble as is evident from the large number of gouges in the turret armour.

8. The KV-2 Model 1940 was popularly called the Dreadnought because of its sheer size. Like the KV-1 tank on which it was based, it suffered from serious mechanical problems, and more were lost to breakdown than enemy action. This vehicle carries the markings of the 12th Panzer Division which put it out of action. (National Archives)

▲ 9

9. A KV-2 Model 1940 knocked out by the side of a road in the Ukraine, 26 August 1941. These KV-2s were greatly feared by German infantry, as their 37mm

▼ 10

anti-tank gun was completely ineffective against its thick armour. (National Archives)

10. A rear view of the KV-2 Model 1940 turret. It was a common Soviet practice to mount an additional 7.62mm machine-gun on the turret rear to protect

against infantry attacks. The large rear hatch was intended primarily for reloading ammunition rather than for crew access.

11. The Su-100Y was a tank-destroyer version of the aborted KV-3 heavy tank project. Neither the tank nor assault gun version entered production, but the SU-100Y prototype took part in the defence of Leningrad in 1941.

12. The 130mm Br-13 gun on the SU-100Y was adapted from a naval gun, although the production version would have used a new gun specifically developed for this role. This front view shows the complicated mantlet and gun cover which provided modest traverse and elevation.

11 ▲   12 ▼

▲ 13   ▼ 14

13. In August 1941, the S.M.Kirov Crane-Transport Plant rebuilt eleven T-26 tanks by removing their turret and superstructure and adding a platform and armoured shield for a 76.2mm regimental gun. This rare photograph shows the turntable being added to one chassis; in the background are several completed vehicles. These improvised artillery vehicles were assigned to the 125th Tank Brigade during the defence of Leningrad.

14. Air defence for Soviet mechanized units was provided by GAZ-AAA lorries mounting a special quadruple 4M 7.62mm Maxim machine-gun mounting. These largely disappeared by 1942 due to the enormous losses during the initial German attacks.

15. One of the rarest self-propelled anti-aircraft vehicles was the GAZ-AAA with a triple DShK 12.7mm anti-aircraft machine-gun mounting. This system was coming into use in 1941, and was not adopted in large numbers.

16. The first serious wartime effort to develop an assault gun was the OSU-76 which mated a ZiS-3 76.2mm divisional gun with T-60 light tank components. Work began in early 1942 at Factory No. 38 in Kirov, but was dropped with the advent of the new T-70 light tank.

15 ▲   16 ▼

17. In the spring of 1942, the SU-12 project began, mating a 76.2mm gun on a modified T-70 light tank chassis. After trials later in the year, it was accepted for production in December as the SU-76 assault gun. The early model seen here during the winter of 1942–3 fighting, was not successful due to the awkward engine configuration. It was replaced in the spring of 1943 by the improved SU-76M.

18. The SU-76M became the definitive wartime version of the SU-76 family. It can be distinguished from the earlier SU-76 by the rear location of the air intakes; on the early SU-76, they were on the centre of the vehicle. The earliest SU-76 formations were independent regiments with twenty-one SU-76, used to support rifle divisions or armies.

▲ 17 ▼ 18

19. A SU-76M in Jihlava, Czechoslovakia, in the spring of 1945. The SU-76M was built in larger numbers than any other Soviet assault gun of the war, some 12,761 being completed up to mid-1945. It didn't become too common on the battlefield until 1944, as some 85 per cent of them were built in 1944–5.

20. An SU-76M crew wearing Caucausian fur caps stand in front of their vehicle during a lull in the fighting near Budapest in 1945. The SU-76M was armed with a derivative of a ZiS-3 76.2mm divisional gun, the most common Soviet artillery piece of the Second World War. It fired the same ammunition as the 76.2mm guns on Soviet tanks.

19 ▲ 20 ▼

▲ 21

21. A column of SU-76M during the fighting in Königsberg on the Baltic in 1945. In May 1944, some Guards rifle divisions began to receive a battalion of twelve SU-76M as standard equipment. In the concluding months of the war, many more of these battalions were added, becoming the normal tactical formation for SU-76s.

▼ 22

22. The lack of top armour was not popular with SU-76M crews. This picture shows a local attempt to add overhead cover.

23. A column of SU-76M during the 1944 fighting. A SU-76M battery consisted of four vehicles, and there were three batteries in each battalion. The light armour and open superstructure led to the derogatory name 'Suka' (bitch) for this vehicle.

24. A pair of SU-76M during the fighting in 1945. By the time that the SU-76M entered widespread service in 1944, its utility in the anti-tank role had greatly diminished due to the arrival of more heavily armoured German tanks like the Panther.

▲ 25 ▼ 26

25. The main reason the SU-76M remained in production was that it was cheap to manufacture and the automotive plants that assembled it could not produce medium tanks. Propulsion came from two GAZ-202 automobile engines. The unusual powerplant arrangement was selected because the manufacturing facilities for the engine already existed, and were cheaper than a new engine design.

26. A battalion of SU-76M lined up in the final year of the war. The SU-76M was second only to the T-34 tank in the total number of Soviet armoured vehicles built during the war.

27. The SU-76 was usually crewed by four men. The normal crew consisted of the gunner, seen at the extreme left; the loader, behind the gunner; and the commander, on the right viewing through a periscope. The fourth crewman, the driver, sat in the forward hull. The crew wear tankers' helmets rather than steel helmets to enable them to use the vehicle's intercom.

28. The SU-76M carried 60 rounds of ammunition, half of it in this ammunition bin in the lower left corner of the fighting compartment. The rest of the ammunition was carried in ready clips on the left side of the fighting compartment and in other bins. Above the ammunition bin are the gunner's sights as well as gun elevation and traverse wheels.

27 ▲ 28 ▼

▲ 29

29. A close-up of the breech of the ZiS-3 76.2mm gun on the ▼ 30

SU-76M. The gunner's sights can be seen on the other side, as well

as one of the vehicle's periscopes.

30. A view looking straight down into the fighting compartment of the SU-76M. The view is slightly distorted because a fish-eye lens was used. The gun is slightly off-set to the left to provide space for the engine's radiator which projects into the right side of the fighting compartment, together with the tunnel for the air-cooling intake. The ready-rack for fifteen more rounds of ammunition can be seen on the left side. The other ammunition racks are for drum magazines for the vehicle's DTM 7.62mm machine-gun.

31. A view of the interior of a well-preserved SU-76M at the East German Army Museum in Dresden. This shows the fighting compartment interior painted in white, which was not the case in wartime. Some of the small details such as intercom fittings, missing from the other vehicle, are seen here.

32. A view of the interior of an SU-76M currently preserved at Aberdeen Proving Ground, in the USA. This vehicle was captured in Korea. The ZiS-3 76mm gun is essentially similar to the towed gun, even the trail lock fittings on the counterweight below the breech slide.

33. In contrast to the cluttered left side of the fighting compartment, the right side is relatively free. The housing on the side wall is the tunnel for the air intake for the radiator. Above it is a storage rack for machine-gun drum magazines.

31 ▲

32 ▲ 33 ▼

35. A view of the engine deck of a SU-76M preserved at the East German Army Museum in Dresden. This shows the location of the tools and other stowage on the upper structure. (Charles Perkins)

36. The SU-76M remained in production in the USSR for a short period after the war. The late-production vehicles had a slightly different rear superstructure shape, the side and rear panels being somewhat higher than the more common version of the SU-76M. This is a Polish LWP vehicle in post-war service.

▲ 34

34. An overview of the SU-76M interior from the rear of the vehicle. This museum vehicle has lost parts over the years, including a small panel of armour plate from the right front corner roof, and the commander's periscope fitting from the right side. This view clearly shows the engine radiator housing and air intake tunnel on the right side.

▲ 35   ▼ 36

37. The 76mm gun on the SU-76M was not entirely satisfactory for use in the tank-destroyer role, leading to the development of the SU-85B, armed with an 85mm LB-2 anti-tank gun in late 1944. As the SU-85 and new SU-100 were more suitable for this role, this vehicle never entered quantity production. This is an artist's concept of the vehicle.

38. The crews of the SU-76 were critical of its unarmoured, open configuration, leading to a design effort to develop a more satisfactory alternative. In the summer of 1943, the Astrov design bureau developed two fully armoured derivatives, the SU-74A/SU-74D with the F-34 76mm gun as seen here, and the SU-74B with the ZiS-2 57mm anti-tank gun. Although both designs offered significant advantages over the basic SU-76M, the Red Army decided to adopt a medium tank destroyer on the T-34 chassis, the SU-85 instead. This is an artist's concept of the SU-76D.

▲ 39

39. Work on an anti-aircraft gun version of the SU-76 paralleled the basic artillery version. This was the initial prototype of the ZSU-37 anti-aircraft vehicle. It shared the engine and transmission problems of the SU-76, and was followed by an improved type based on the SU-76M hull.

▼ 40

Quite remarkably, at least ... SU-76i was captured by ... n troops, and saw action ... n Europe during the ... 944. The meaning of ... ffix has never been ... but probably ... rmy (foreign) or ...). (James ...

... stroyers

... T48

... the ... in in ... 1945 and ... a German Grille ... mm howitzer vehicle with a 30mm Flak 103 autocannon substituted for the usual howitzer. (James Loop)

42. The Russians captured relatively large numbers of German Pz KpfwIII tanks and the related StuG.III assault guns during the war. In January 1943, a design team under G.I.Kashtanov of the Central Administration of Tank Rebuilding was assigned the task of rearming the captured vehicles with standard Soviet weapons. A simple fixed casemate was designed, mounting the F-34 76mm tank gun. This vehicle was designated SU-76i. While most were used by training units, some actually saw combat. This vehicle, preserved in the Ukraine, fell through the ice while crossing the River Sluch near Sarny on 11 January 1944 while supporting the 143rd Rifle Division. (George Balin)

43. An overhead view of the SU-76i. As can be seen, the vehicle was fully enclosed, unlike the normal SU-76M. A second type was built, the SU-122i, mounting a 122mm Model 1938 howitzer. However, photographs of this enigmatic vehicle have never been released. Russian sources claim that 1,200 SU-76i and Su-122i were built although this may include efforts after the war. (George Balin)

41 ▲

42 ▲   43 ▼

44
one
Germa
in Easte
winter of
the SU-76i
fully explained
stood for *inostra*
izmennik (turnco
Loop)

45. Among the tank-de
received from Lend-Leas
shipments was the America
57mm Gun Motor Carriage.
Russians called these SU-57 an
used them in special tank-
destroyer brigades, each unit
having sixty of these half-tracks.
The SU-57 was armed with the
M1 57mm anti-tank gun, based
on the British 6-pounder. (Ivan
Bajtos)

▲44 ▼45

PERFORMANCE OF SOVIET ASSAULT GUN WEAPONS

Designation	76.2mm ZiS-3	85mm D-5S	100mm D-10S	122mm M-30S	122mm A-19S D-25S	152mm ML-20S
Barrel length	L/42.5	L/54.6	L/56	L/22.7	L/46.3	L/28.8
Armour-piercing (HE) round	BR-350A	BR-365	BR-412	—	BR-471B	BR-540
weight (kg)	6.3	9.02	15.6	—	24.9	48.7
initial muzzle vel (m/s)	655	792	1000	—	800	600
penetration at 500m (mm)	69	111	195	—	145	124
penetration at 1,000m (mm)	61	102	185	—	145	124
Armour-piercing (DS) round	BR-350P	BR-365P	—	—	—	—
weight (kg)	3.0	4.9	—	—	—	—
initial muzzle vel (m/s)	965	1,200	—	—	—	—
penetration at 500m (mm)	92	138	—	—	—	—
penetration at 1,000m (mm)	60	100	—	—	—	—
HEAT round	BR-353A	—	—	BP-460A	BP-460A	—
weight (kg)	3.94	—	—	13.2	13.2	—
initial muzzle vel (m/s)	325	—	—	335	550	—
penetration, any range (mm)	75	—	—	200	200	—
High-explosive round	F-534	—	F-412	F-460	F-460	OF-530
weight (kg)	6.23	—	15.8	22.6	22.6	40.0
initial muzzle vel (m/s)	680	—	900	515	800	655
HE-fragmentation round	OF-350	O-365K	—	OF-471	OF-471	OF-540
weight (kg)	6.21	9.2	—	24.9	24.9	43.7
initial muzzle vel (m/s)	680	792	—	515	800	655

Weight refers to projectile and not entire round; penetration performance is against vertical steel armour plate.

TABLES OF EQUIPMENT OF SOVIET ASSAULT GUN UNITS, 1943–5

Mechanized Artillery Units	Date	Troops	Batteries	HQ Tank	SU-76	SU-85	SU-100	SU-122	SU-152, ISU-152 ISU-122
SP Artillery Regt	Jan 43		6	—	17	—	—	8	—
Light SP Artillery Regt	May 43		4	—	21	—	—	—	—
Light SP Artillery Regt	May 43		3	—	12	—	—	—	—
Med SP Artillery Regt	May 43		4	T-34	—	—	—	16	—
Heavy SP Artillery Regt	May 43		4	KV	—	—	—	—	12
Heavy SP Artillery Regt	Aug 43		4	KV	—	—	—	—	21
Ind SP Artillery Regt	Aug 43		3	—	13	—	—	—	—
Tank Destroyer Bn	Aug 43		3	T-34	—	16	—	—	—
Tank Destroyer Bn	1944		3	T-34	—	21	—	—	—
Tank Destroyer Bn	1945		3	T-34	—	—	21	—	—
Guards Heavy SP Arty Bde	Dec 44	1,804	12	—	3	—	—	—	65
Guards SP Arty Bde	Dec 44	1,492	12	—	3	—	65	—	—

SOVIET ASSAULT GUN PRODUCTION

	1942	1943	1944	1945	Total
SU-76	26	1928	7155	3562	12671
SU-122	25	630	493		1148
SU-85		750	1300		2050
SU-100			500	1175	1675
SU-152		704			704
ISU-122/ISU-152		35	2510	1530	4075
Annual Total	51	4047	11958	6267	22323
SU Production as percentage of total Soviet AFV	0.2%	17%	41%	24%	

*SU-76 figures include ZSU-37 production; 1945 figures refer to first six months.

TECHNICAL DATA FOR SOVIET ASSAULT GUNS, 1942–5

Designation	SU-76	SU-76M	SU-85	SU-100	SU-122	SU-152	ISU-122	ISU-152
Crew	4	4	4	4	5	5	5	5
Weight (tonnes)	11.2	10.2	29.2	31.6	30.9	45.5	45.5	46
Length (cm)	500	500	815	945	695	895	985	918
Width (cm)	274	270	300	300	300	325	307	307
Height (cm)	220	210	245	225	232	245	248	248
Armament	ZiS-3	ZiS-3	D-5S	D-10S	M-30S	ML-20S	A-19S	ML-20S
Gun calibre (mm)	76.2	76.2	85	100	122	152	122	152
Main rounds stowed	60	60	48	34	40	20	30	20
Engine type	2 × GAZ-202	2 × GAZ-203	V-2	V-2	V-2	V-2	V-2	V-2
Horsepower	70 + 70	85 + 85	500	500	500	600	600	600
Fuel (litres)	400	420	810	770	810	975	860	860
Max road speed (km/h)	44	45	47	48	55	43	37	37
Max road range (km)	265	320	400	320	300	330	220	220
Max terrain range (km)	160	190	200	180	150	120	80	80

SU-152 HEAVY ASSAULT GUN

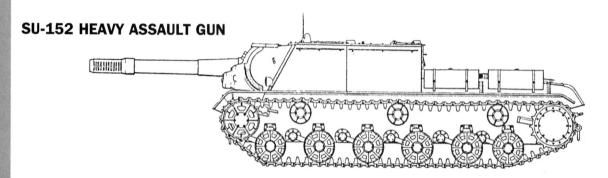

ISU-122s HEAVY ASSAULT GUN

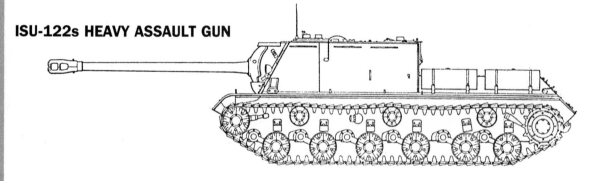

ISU-152 HEAVY ASSAULT GUN

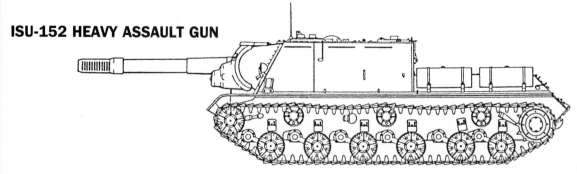

Janusz Magnuski

Designation	SU-76	SU-76M	SU-85	SU-100	SU-122	SU-152	ISU-122	ISU-152
Armour (mm)								
hull front	35	35	45	45	45	60	90	90
hull side	16	16	45	45	45	60	90	90
hull rear	16	16	45	45	45	60	60	60
hull roof	10	10	20	20	20	30	30	30
hull bottom	10	10	20	20	20	30	30	30
Radio type	9R	9RM	9R	10-RF-26	9R	9R	10RF	10RF

SU-76M LIGHT ASSAULT GUN

SU-85 TANK DESTROYER

SU-100 TANK DESTROYER

SU-57 (T-48) LIGHT TANK DESTROYER

Janusz Magnuski

▲ 46

46. The first assault gun based on the T-34 tank chassis was the SU-122. The first of these was completed at the end of 1942 and went into action in January 1943 in the Leningrad area. The early assault gun regiments were based on four batteries of SU-76 and two of SU-122 and proved to be a tactical failure. However, the SU-122, because of its better armour protection, proved quite popular for close infantry support.

47. The Germans captured an SU-122 in 1943 and sent it back for evaluation. It was armed with a derivative of the M-30 122mm howitzer. From May 1943 onward, the SU-122 served in medium self-propelled artillery regiments (with sixteen SU-122 each), used primarily to support rifle divisions.

▼ 47

48. This front view of an SU-122 provides a very clear view of the massive cast mantlet and recuperator of the SU-122. Note that the driver's hatch has been reduced to only half the width of the normal tank hatch. A total of 1,148 SU-122 were built during the war, not counting the SU-122i built on captured German chassis. The final production batches of the SU-122 used the same ball mantlet as the SU-85.

49. The first dedicated tank-destroyer developed for the Red Army during the war was the SU-85. The SU-85 mated the new D-5T 85mm gun to the T-34 Model 1943 hull. It was developed beginning in 1943 and entered service in the late summer after the climatic Kursk–Orel counter-offensive. Initially, SU-85 tank-destroyer battalions had sixteen SU-85 each, but this was expanded to twenty-one by 1945.

▲50 ▼51

324

Zasługi
bojowe:

Szlak
bojowy:

SMOLEŃSK · ŻYTOMIERZ · ŁUCK
CHEŁM · LUBLIN · PRAGA
WARSZAWA
BYDGOSZCZ
ZŁOTÓW
JAROSŁAWIEC
CZAPLINEK
GRYFICE
KAMIEŃ POMORSKI
ODRA
ŁABA

Przeszedł w bojach 4980 KM

52 ▲

50. A close-up of the ball mantlet of the SU-85 on a vehicle currently preserved at the Polish Army Museum in Warsaw. The main gun did not have a coaxial machine-gun, so a small pistol port was provided above the driver's hatch. Crews usually carried a DTM 7.62mm machine-gun or PPSh submachine-guns for vehicle defence.

51. A side view of the SU-85 number 324 at the museum in Warsaw. The silhouettes on the front record its claims during its combat career in 1944–5. It served with the 13th SP Artillery Regiment beginning in the summer of 1944. It was knocked out twice, on 10 February 1945 near Klosowo, and again on 3 March 1945 near Wierzchowo, and battle damage can still be seen on the mantlet and right side.

52. An SU-85 with the spoke-style roadwheels, in Polish service in the 1950s. A total of 2,050 SU-85s were built during the war, being replaced on the assembly lines by the SU-100 in 1944. With the appearance of the German Panther tank, it was decided that a heavier weapon was needed.

53. An SU-85 of the Polish 13th SP Artillery Regiment which took part in the fighting in Germany in 1945. Although difficult to see in this photograph, the superstructure is surrounded by a white band and there is a white cross on the roof. These were air recognition signs during the final weeks of the war around Berlin. Also on the superstructure side is a white triangle, the marking which was supposed to replace the bands after American fighter-bombers reported spotting German vehicles painted with Soviet white air ID bands.

53 ▼

▲ 54

▲ 55 ▼ 56

54. A well-camouflaged Polish SU-85 on the way to the front. The Polish People's Army had two SU-85 regiments during the war, the 13th and 28th, receiving about 70 vehicles from the USSR. The Czechoslovak Army also used the SU-85, but in smaller numbers.

55. The final production batches of the SU-85 had the modernized superstructure developed for the SU-100. It was characterized by the commander's large circular pulpit added on the right side of the superstructure.

56. The appearance of the Panther tank in 1943, and the Royal Tiger in 1944, forced the Russians to adopt a heavier gun in their tank-destroyers. In 1944, they decided to develop a 100mm gun, designated the D-10, which was mounted on a modified T-34-85 chassis. Although closely resembling the SU-85, a new commander's station was added to the right side, and the mantlet was considerably enlarged to accommodate the new gun. The first SU-100 were produced in September 1944, and first saw extensive action in the fighting in Poland in January 1945. These Soviet SU-100 are taking a breather following the end of the fighting in Czechoslovakia in May 1945. (Ivan Bajtos)

57. A battery of SU-100 ambushed by German forces in the fighting on the outskirts of Brno in May 1945. The large size of the 100mm rounds meant that only 34 could be carried compared to 48 on the SU-85. The 100mm gun on the SU-100 was later used on the T-54 and T-55 tanks of the 1950s. (Ivan Bajtos)

58. An SU-100 in Czechoslovakia at the end of the war. In December 1944, the Red Army began forming Guards mechanized artillery brigades, equipped with 65 SU-100. These were used as shock units by Soviet tank armies during the offensive operations in January/February 1945.

▲ 59

59. A close-up of a preserved SU-100 in a museum in Poland. This view clearly shows the structural differences from the SU-85 to SU-100, notably the new commander's station, and the prominent mushroom vents.

Interestingly enough, this vehicle has a swivel pot for a radio antenna located behind the commander's station in lieu of the usual location above the national white eagle insignia.

60. The SU-100 was extremely cramped inside as is evident from this view of the driver's and gunner's stations. The gunner operated immediately behind the driver, and to the lower right can be seen ammunition stowage

racks under the gun. (Joseph Bermudez)

61. The massive D-10S gun removed from an SU-100. The loader operated on the right side of the gun, behind the commander, and most of the ammunition was stowed on the rear walls of the fighting compartment. (Joseph Bermudez)

62. After the war, the SU-100 remained in production in the USSR, and later entered production in Czechoslovakia. The post-war SU-100M version had some small changes, notably the addition of a large stowage bin on the right fender, as seen on this preserved SU-100M in Kiev.

▼ 60

▲ 63

63. This overhead view of a Czechoslovak SU-100M clearly shows the added stowage bin as well as other minor construction differences on this model such as the reconfigured hand-holds.

64. The SU-100M saw combat use in the Middle East wars in 1956, 1967 and 1973 with Egyptian and Syrian forces. These SU-100M (of Czechoslovak manufacture) are on parade in Egypt.

65. The first of the heavy assault guns was this curious KV-6. It mounted a single 76mm gun in the centre, and two 45mm anti-tank guns on each side. It is unclear what advantage the designers saw in adding two

45mm guns to the combination, as their effectiveness in anti-tank fighting by 1942 was very dubious. A similar vehicle, the KV-7, mounted twin 76mm guns, and almost entered production in January 1942.

▼ 64

66. A far more reasonable assault gun design appeared at the end of 1942, mounting the 152mm ML-20 gun-howitzer on the KV-1S chassis. An even heavier version, mounting a 203mm howitzer, was considered but eventually abandoned. The first SU-152 entered service in May 1943. Their effectiveness against the German Tiger, Panther and Elephant led to the nickname Zvierboi (animal hunter).

▲ 67

▲ 68 ▼ 69

67. A rear view of an SU-152 captured by the Germans. The small numerals painted on the hull refer to armour thickness and angle. This clearly shows that the SU-152 was built on the modified KV-1S hull, which was characterized by a rear engine deck with a more pronounced downward angle.

68. The SU-152 was one of the rarer Soviet assault guns, only 704 being built, in 1943. At least one remains as a monument in the USSR today.

69. The SU-152 closely resembled the ISU-152 which succeeded it. It can be distinguished by the lower superstructure sides and KV bow. This memorial vehicle was obviously assembled from odds and ends because the wheels are the early-style wheels which were not used on SU-152s when first built.

70. An overhead view of a SU-152 captured by the Germans. The large rear hatch was used mainly for loading ammunition, the front hatches being used by the crew. The SU-152 carried only twenty rounds of ammunition because of the sheer size of the large projectiles and their separate casings.

71. As the KV was phased out of production, and the new IS heavy tank took its place, the ISU-152 replaced the SU-152. The ISU-152 was configured much like the SU-152, but the superstructure was noticeably higher. This particular ISU-152 served with the Polish Army in the 1950s.

70 ▲

71 ▼

▲72

74. The ISU-152 remained in service in the Warsaw Pact for many years after the war, like this Polish Army vehicle. This view clearly shows the 12.7mm DShK machine-gun added to the ISU-152 for anti-aircraft protection.

75. The 122mm A-19 towed gun was mounted on the same carriage as the 152mm ML-20 gun. As a result, it was a simple matter to adapt the 122mm gun to the ISU, resulting in the ISU-122. The Russians decided to produce both a 122mm and 152mm ISU simply because there was an existing inventory of both gun tubes as well as suitable ammunition. The 122mm gun had better anti-tank performance, while the 152mm gun howitzer offered a larger high-explosive projectile when engaging non-armoured targets.

72. Although the ISU-152 was a very massive vehicle, the interior was cramped because of the sheer size of the ML-20S howitzer, and the ammunition stowage. This is a view of the

▼ 73

driver's and gunner's stations to the left of the gun. (Charles Kliment)

73. An overhead view of the ISU-152 superstructure roof. The

ISU-152 had the large rear ammunition hatch in the same location as the SU-152, but the two front hatches were modernized using traversable split hatches. The right side

hatch was fitted for a 12.7mm DShK heavy AA machine-gun mounting. (Charles Kliment)

▲ 76   ▼ 77

76. The ISU-122 was used in the same fashion as the ISU-152, in heavy mechanized artillery brigades with either 65 ISU-122 or ISU-152. Usually each tank army had one of these brigades for heavy direct fire support. These vehicles were not generally used for indirect fire, but reserved for breakthrough operations to support tank formations.

77. An ISU-122 of the Polish Army on post-war exercises. The beams carried on the sides are being dropped into anti-tank ditches as fascines to facilitate the advance of other vehicles.

78. Although the original version of the ISU-122 used the ordinary 122mm A-19 gun, in 1944 the Petrov bureau developed the D-25 tank gun which had a drop-breech. This was easier and faster to use in the confined interior of an assault gun, and it was adopted on the final production batches of the ISU-122, called the ISU-122S. This version also introduced other features, such as a new ball mantlet cover and a muzzle brake on the gun. This is a Polish Army vehicle.

79. A clear view of the new convex armoured mantlet adopted on the ISU-122S and the new D-25S gun. This gun was essentially similar to the D-25T gun used on the related IS-2 heavy tank. The large hole in the mantlet is for the gunner's telescopic sight.

80. An interesting overhead view of an ISU-122S on parade in Poland after the war. The five 'x's on the barrel are kill markings, the ISU-122S having served with the Polish 25th Self-Propelled Artillery Regiment beginning in December 1944.

78 ▲

79 ▲   80 ▼

▲ 81   ▼ 82

81. The Red Army made extensive use of vehicle-mounted multiple artillery rocket-launchers during the war, nicknamed 'Katyusha' (Little Katie) after a popular song of the time. They were officially called Guards Mortars. This BM-13 consists of eight twin rails for sixteen 132mm rockets, mounted on a ZiS-6 truck. This was the first mobile Katyusha to see service, being first used in July 1941. This vehicle is currently preserved in Leningrad. (Esa Muikku)

82. The BM-13 was later followed by the BM-8-36 which could fire thirty-six 82mm rockets in a single salvo. This particular Katyusha is mounted on a ZiS-6 truck, although other Soviet and Lend-Lease trucks were also used. (Esa Muikku)

83. In 1942, some BM-8-24 mountings were fitted to T-40 and T-60 light tank chassis. This particular example was mounted on a T-60 chassis and was knocked out by the Germans. (T. Wagner)

84. A special light mountain Katyusha was also built, the BM-8-8, which could be broken-down for mule or horse transport. It was occasionally vehicle-mounted.

▲ 85 ▼ 86

85. One of the rarer vehicle-mounted Katyushas was the BM-8-8 mountain artillery launcher, fitted to Lend-Lease Jeeps.

86. The most common Katyusha platform in 1944–5 was the Lend-Lease Studebaker US6 truck. This particular example is a BM-31-12, which fired the larger M-30 rocket. The frame launcher is covered under a tarpaulin in this view. (Esa Muikku)

87. The BM-13-16 launcher was mounted on a wide variety of vehicles, one of the rarer examples being this unit using Lend-Lease US General Motors COE trucks. (James Loop)

88. A Victory Day parade in Moscow's Red Square showing the open-frame launchers for the BM-31-12 on Studebaker trucks. The M-30 rocket did not appear on a self-propelled mounting until relatively late in the war, 1944. Previously, it was fired from static wooden-frame launchers.

The *Fotofax* series

A new range of pictorial studies of military subjects for the modeller, historian and enthusiast. Each title features a carefully-selected set of photographs plus a data section of facts and figures on the topic covered. With line drawings and detailed captioning, every volume represents a succinct and valuable study of the subject. New and forthcoming titles:

Warbirds
F-111 Aardvark
P-47 Thunderbolt
B-52 Stratofortress
Stuka!
Jaguar
US Strategic Air Power:
  Europe 1942–1945
Dornier Bombers
RAF in Germany

Vintage Aircraft
German Naval Air Service
Sopwith Camel
Fleet Air Arm, 1920–1939
German Bombers of WWI

Soldiers
World War One: 1914
World War One: 1915
World War One: 1916
Union Forces of the American
  Civil War
Confederate Forces of the
  American Civil War
Luftwaffe Uniforms
British Battledress 1945–1967
  (2 vols)

Warships
Japanese Battleships, 1897–
1945
Escort Carriers of World War
Two
German Battleships, 1897–
1945
Soviet Navy at War, 1941–1945
US Navy in World War Two,
1943–1944
US Navy, 1946–1980 (2 vols)
British Submarines of World
  War One

Military Vehicles
The Chieftain Tank
Soviet Mechanized Firepower
Today
British Armoured Cars since
1945
NATO Armoured Fighting
Vehicles
The Road to Berlin
NATO Support Vehicles

The *Illustrated* series

The internationally successful range of photo albums devoted to current, recent and historic topics, compiled by leading authors and representing the best means of obtaining your own photo archive.

Warbirds
US Spyplanes
USAF Today
Strategic Bombers, 1945–1985
Air War over Germany
Mirage
US Naval and Marine Aircraft
  Today
USAAF in World War Two
B-17 Flying Fortress
Tornado
Junkers Bombers of World War
  Two
Argentine Air Forces in the
  Falklands Conflict
F-4 Phantom Vol II
Army Gunships in Vietnam
Soviet Air Power Today
F-105 Thunderchief
Fifty Classic Warbirds
Canberra and B-57
German Jets of World War Two

Vintage Warbirds
The Royal Flying Corps in
  World War One
German Army Air Service in
  World War One
RAF between the Wars
The Bristol Fighter
Fokker Fighters of World War
  One
Air War over Britain, 1914–
  1918
Nieuport Aircraft of World War
  One

Tanks
Israeli Tanks and Combat
  Vehicles
Operation Barbarossa
Afrika Korps
Self-Propelled Howitzers
British Army Combat Vehicles
  1945 to the Present
The Churchill Tank
US Mechanized Firepower
  Today
Hitler's Panzers
Panzer Armee Afrika
US Marine Tanks in World War
  Two

Warships
The Royal Navy in 1980s
The US Navy Today
NATO Navies of the 1980s
British Destroyers in World
  War Two
Nuclear Powered Submarines
Soviet Navy Today
British Destroyers in World
  War One
The World's Aircraft Carriers,
1914–1945
The Russian Convoys, 1941–
1945
The US Navy in World War
Two
British Submarines in World
  War Two
British Cruisers in World War
One
U-Boats of World War Two
Malta Convoys, 1940–1943

Uniforms
US Special Forces of World
  War Two
US Special Forces 1945 to the
  Present
The British Army in Northern
  Ireland
Israeli Defence Forces, 1948 to
  the Present
British Special Forces, 1945 to
  Present
US Army Uniforms Europe,
  1944–1945
The French Foreign Legion
Modern American Soldier
Israeli Elite Units
US Airborne Forces of World
  War Two
The Boer War
The Commandos World War
  Two to the Present
Victorian Colonial Wars

A catalogue listing these series and other Arms & Armour Press titles is available on request from: Sales Department, Arms & Armour Press, Artillery House, Artillery Row, London SW1P 1RT.